Journeys Through the Alef-Bet

A Hebrew Pre-Primer

Torah Aura Productions

ISBN #1-891662-65-1

Copyright © 2005 Torah Aura Productions

Photographs by Mark Robert Halper and Josh Barkin.

Torah Aura Productions • 4423 Fruitland Avenue, Los Angeles, CA 90058

(800) BE-Torah • (800) 238-6724 • (323) 585-7312 • fax (323) 585-0327

E-MAIL <misrad@torahaura.com> • Visit the Torah Aura website at www.torahaura.com

MANUFACTURED IN CHINA

Meet the שִׁין (Shin)

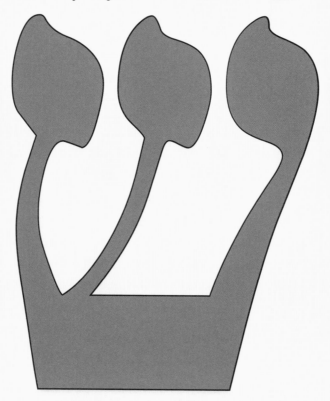

Your teacher will help you meet these שׁ words.

שָׁלוֹם	שַׁבָּת	שׁוּשָׁן	שׁוֹפָר

3

Practice these שׁ letters by saying the sound each letter makes. ◀▪▪▪▪▪

שׁ   שׁ   שׁ   שׁ   שׁ   שׁ   .1

שׁ   שׁ   שׁ   שׁ   שׁ   שׁ   .2

Cross out each letter that is not a שׁ. ◀▪▪▪▪▪

שׁ   שׁ   שׁ   שׁ   ✗   שׁ   .3

שׁ   שׁ   ✗   שׁ   שׁ   שׁ   .4

שׁ   שׁ   ✗   שׁ   שׁ   ✗   .5

✗   ✗   שׁ   שׁ   ✗   ✗   .6

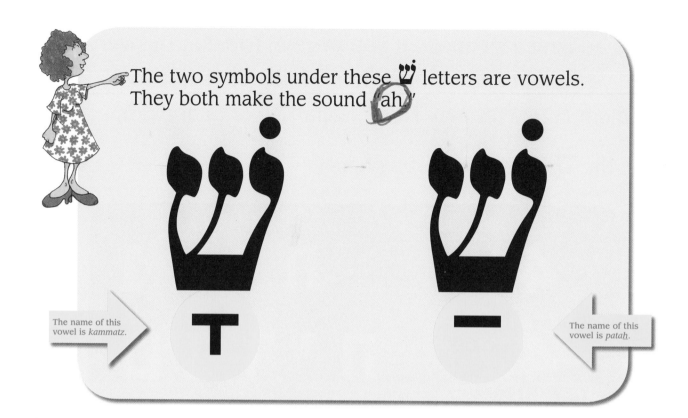

The two symbols under these ש letters are vowels. They both make the sound "ah"

The name of this vowel is *kammatz*.

The name of this vowel is *patah*.

Practice sounding out these combinations of שָ and שַ.

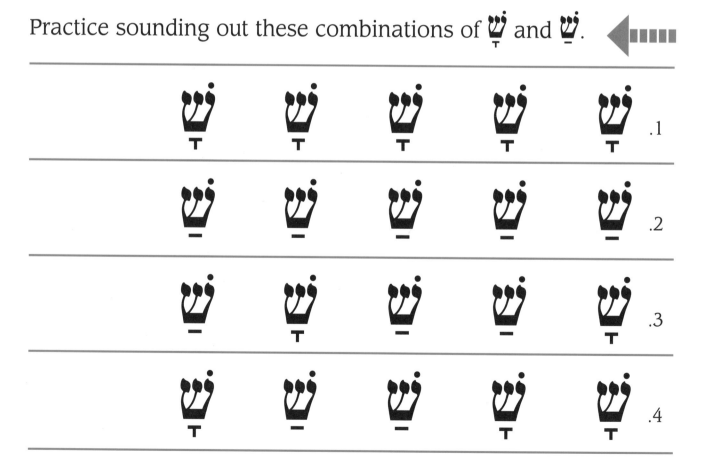

.1

.2

.3

.4

This is an Israeli signpost. If you were in Israel at this very place, you could find out how many kilometers it is to Jerusalem (126), Tel Aviv (134), Haifa (79) or Eilat (356).

Circle the  letters on this signpost.

Meet the בֵּית (Bet)

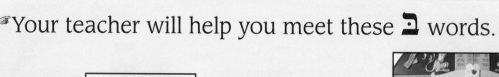

Your teacher will help you meet these **ב** words.

בֵּית   בְּרֵאשִׁית   בֵּית כְּנֶסֶת   בִּימָה

Trace these **ב** letters and then make two of your own.

Practice these **ב** letters by saying the sound each letter makes.

     .1

Now add in the **שׁ**.

.2

Someone spilled the Alef-Bet soup. Circle every **ב** in this bowl.

Practice sounding out these combinations of שָׁ, שַׁ, בָּ and בַּ.

בָּ   בַּ   בָּ   בַּ   בָּ   .1

שַׁ   בָּ   שַׁ   שָׁ   בַּ   .2

שַׁ   שַׁ   בָּ   בַּ   שַׁ   .3

שָׁ   בַּ   בָּ   שָׁ   בַּ   .4

Find and circle the בּ letters.

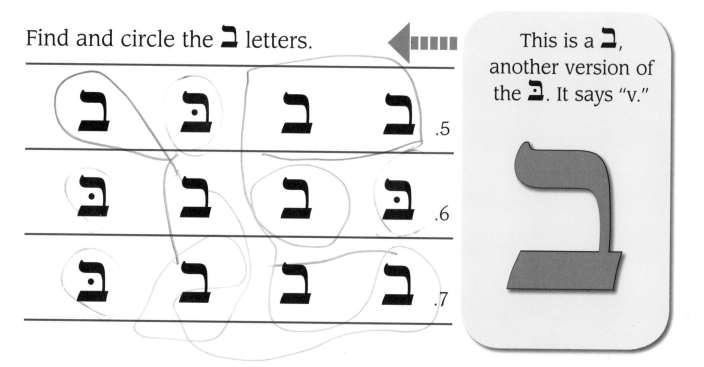

This is a בּ, another version of the בּ. It says "v."

ב   ב   בּ   ב   .5

בּ   ב   ב   בּ   .6

בּ   ב   ב   ב   .7

This company is building homes on this corner.
Israelis don't use vowels or dots in the letters so
a **בּ** will look like a **ב**. That's okay—they are the
same letter.
Circle all the **ב** letters on this sign.

Meet the תָו (Tav)

Your teacher will help you meet these ת words.

תּוֹרָה   תַּלְמוּד תּוֹרָה   תְּפִילִין   תַּפּוּחַ

Practice these ת letters by saying the sound each letter makes. ◄▮▮▮▮▮

תּ   תּ   תּ   תּ   תּ .1

Now add in the שׁ and the בּ. ◄▮▮▮▮▮

תּ   תּ   שׁ   בּ   תּ .2

שׁ   תּ   תּ   בּ   שׁ .3

Draw a box around the letters that are the same on each line. ◄▮▮▮▮▮

פּ   תּ   שׁ   כ   תּ .4

בּ   כ   ב   בּ   ל .5

ע   מ   שׁ   ט   שׁ .6

Circle the תּ and draw a box around the ת.

תּ (boxed)	תּ (circled)	שׁ (crossed)	ת (circled)	.1
בּ (crossed)	ת (circled)	תּ (boxed)	תּ (circled)	.2
ת (circled)	בּ (crossed)	תּ (boxed)	שׁ (crossed)	.3

Sometimes the תּ has a dot (*dagesh*) in it and sometimes it doesn't. Both תּ and ת sound the same.

Practice sounding out these combinations.

תָּ	תַ	תָ	תַּ	תָּ .4
תַ	בָ	תַּ	בָּ	שַׁ .5
שֵׁ	שָׁ	תַ	תַּ .6	
תַּ	בָּ	שָׁ	תַּ .7	
בַ	שַׁ	בַ	שָׁ .8	

Can you sound out this word?

שַׁבָּת

13

Want to park your car in Jerusalem?

Park your car and then circle all the ת letters on this building.

Remember that ת and ת are the same letter.

Meet the  לָמֶד (Lamed)

Your teacher will help you meet these ל words.

לוֹמֵד   לֶחֶם   לֵב   לוּלָב

Trace these ל letters and then make two of your own.

Practice these ל letters by saying the sound each letter makes.
Then add in the other letters you know.

ל　　ל　　ל　　ל　　ל　　ל　.1

תּ　　בּ　　ל　　תּ　　ל　　שׁ　.2

Circle the letter to complete the pattern in each row.
Then say aloud all the sounds on each row.

בּ　שׁ　ל　＿＿＿　בּ　ל　שׁ　בּ　ל　.3

תּ　שׁ　ל　＿＿＿　ל　תּ　שׁ　ל　תּ　.4

בּ　שׁ　תּ　＿＿＿　תּ　בּ　בּ　תּ　שׁ　.5

16

The character next to the ל is a vowel. It makes the sound "oh."

The name of this vowel is _holom_.

Practice sounding out these letters and vowels.

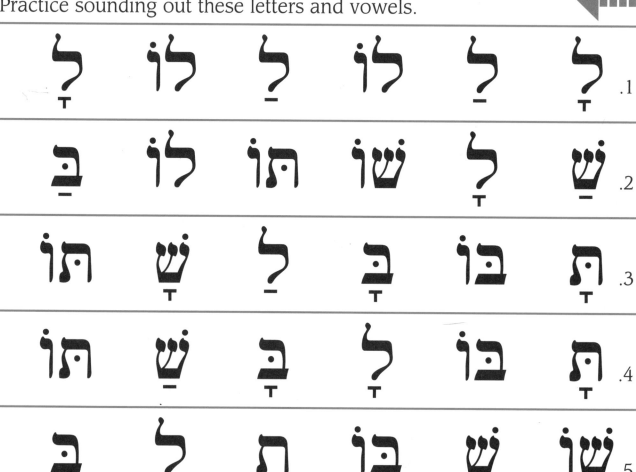

לַ	לוֹ	לַ	לוֹ	לַ	לָ .1
בַּ	לוֹ	תוֹ	שׁוֹ	לָ	שָׁ .2
תוֹ	שָׁ	לַ	בָּ	בּוֹ	תָּ .3
תוֹ	שַׁ	בָּ	לָ	בּוֹ	תָּ .4
בָּ	לַ	תַּ	בּוֹ	שָׁ	שׁוֹ .5

Here we are at the corner of Ramban and Ben Maimon.
Circle all the ל letters you find.

Meet the מֶם (Mem)

Your teacher will help you meet these מ words.

מוֹרָה   מְזוּזָה   מְגִלָּה   מַצָּה

19

Trace these מ letters and then make two of your own.

Practice these מ letters by saying the sound each letter makes. Then add in the other letters you know.

1. מ   מ   מ   מ   מ   מ

2. מ   ב   מ   ת   ל   מ

3. ת   מ   בּ   ל   מ   שׁ

Tic Tac Toe. You must correctly say the sound of each letter before you can claim the square. Be careful, there are some alternate letters. If you have time, play another round.

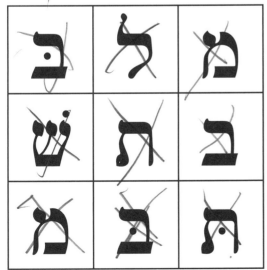

20

Circle the **מ** and draw a box around the **ם**.

1. ם מ ם מ מ מ
2. מ ת ם ל
3. שׁ ת מ ם

This is a **ם** *sofit*. *Sofit* means "end." This **ם** is only used at the end of a word.

Practice sounding out these combinations.

4. מָ מַ מוֹ מוֹ מַ מָ
5. מוֹ תַ בַ תוֹ בָ שַׁ
6. תַ שָׁ מוֹ לַ
7. שׁוֹ לוֹ לָ מַ
8. בַּ שָׁם

Can you sound out this word?

שָׁלוֹם

Bonus Points!!!
Try sounding out these two "words."

בָּם שָׁם

21

Here's a kosher restaurant to eat at. This one is located at the great synagogue in Jerusalem.

Circle all the מ letters you find. Don't forget the ם *sofit*.

Meet the דָּלֶת (Dalet)

 Your teacher will help you meet these ד words.

דֹב

דֶּגֶל

דְּבַשׁ

דֶּלֶת

ד ד ד ד ד ד

Practice these ד letters and other letters you know by saying
the sound each letter makes.

ד ד ד ד ד ד .1

ד בּ מ תּ ד ל .2

תּ מ ד ל ד שׁ .3

Circle the letters that are the same.

א ד ג א ד .4

ג בּ בּ ד בּ .5

ג ד בּ ב ד .6

Sound out the Hebrew on each line.
Color in the circle if all the sounds on the line are the same.

◯ .1	דָ	דַ	דַ	דַ	דָ
◯ .2	תּוֹ	תּוֹ	תּוֹ	תּוֹ	תּוֹ
◯ .3	לְ	לַ	לָ	לֶ	לָ
◯ .4	שֶׁ	מָ	מַ	מַ	מָ
◯ .5	דוֹ	דוֹ	דוֹ	דוֹ	דוֹ

Your teacher will say a sound for each of these lines.
Be the first to circle it!

תַ .6	דַ	מָ	לָ	שֶׁ	בַּ
שׁוֹ .7	תּוֹ	דוֹ	בּוֹ	מוֹ	לוֹ
דוֹ .8	שֶׁ	בַּ	מוֹ	דָם	דֶם	דָם

25

מעבדה

לתקוני רדיו, דיסק
לרכב ולבית
תיקון חלון ונעילה
חשמלית לרכב
טל. 02-6250030

Looking for a handy person to repair your electric train? Call this number in Jerusalem.

But first circle all the ד letters you find.

Meet the אָלֶף (Alef)

Your teacher will help you meet these א words.

אֲרוֹן־ הַקּוֹדֶשׁ

אָדָם

אֶחָד

אֶתְרוֹג

Trace these **א** letters and then make two of your own.

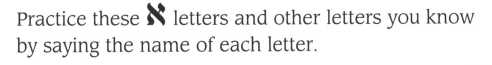

Practice these **א** letters and other letters you know by saying the name of each letter.

א	א	א	א	א	א	.1
ד	בּ	א	תּ	א	ל	.2
שׁ	מ	ל	ד	בּ	א	.3
א	ל	תּ	ד	א	מ	.4
ד	מ	ל	תּ	בּ	שׁ	.5

The symbol under the **א** is a vowel. It makes the sound "ee."

The name of this vowel is *ḥirik*.

Practice the letters you know with the new vowel .

בְּ	לְ תְּ	דְ	מֶ	אִ	.1
תוֹ	אוֹ	מַ	אִ	בָּ	אַ	.2
בְ	בּוֹ	מָ	דָ	לוֹ	שָׁ	.3
אָב שׁוֹ	אַ	מוֹ	תְּ	בִּ	.4

Are you hungry? We can stop and have a snack at this vegetarian kosher restaurant that serves fish. Circle all the א letters you find.

Meet the נוּן (Nun)

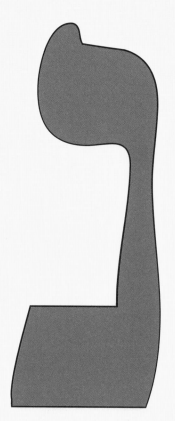

Your teacher will help you meet these נ words.

נָחָשׁ   נֵר תָּמִיד   נֵרוֹת   נֵר

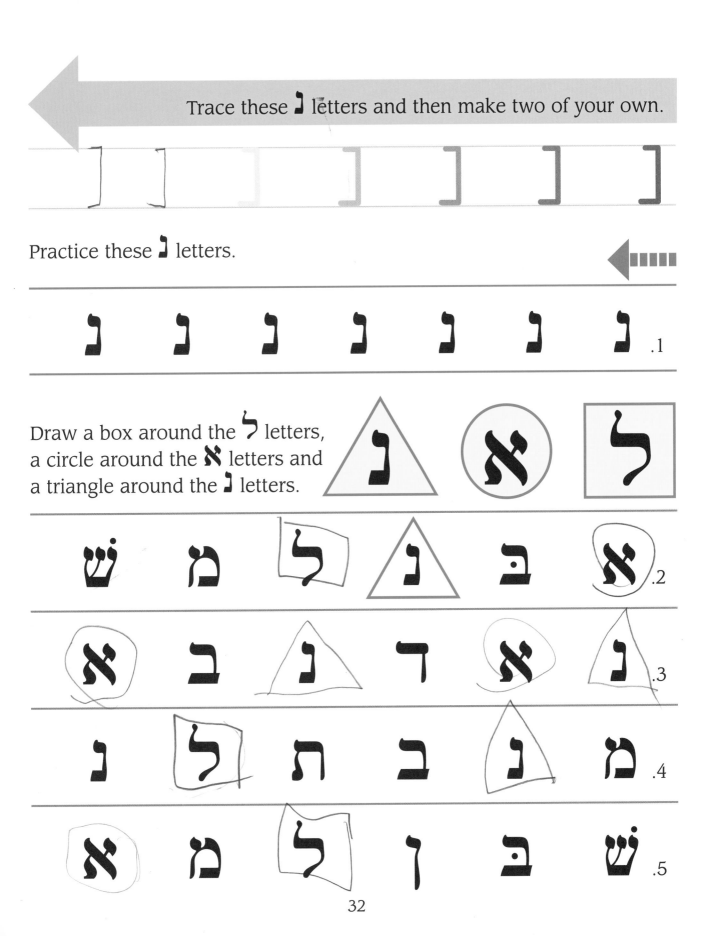

Trace these נ letters and then make two of your own.

Practice these נ letters.

נ   נ   נ   נ   נ   נ   .1

Draw a box around the ל letters,
a circle around the א letters and
a triangle around the נ letters.

שׁ   מ   ל   נ   ב   א   .2

א   ב   נ   ד   א   נ   .3

נ   ל   ת   ב   נ   מ   .4

א   מ   ל   ן   ב   שׁ   .5

32

Circle the נ and draw a box around the ן.

This is a נ *sofit*.
Sofit means "end."
This ן is only used at the end of a word.

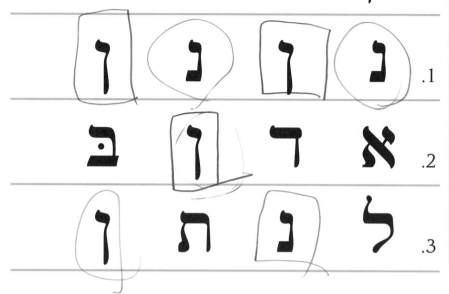

1. נ ו נ | נ ו נ | נ | ו

2. ב | ד | ו | ד | א

3. ו | ת | נ | ל

Practice sounding out these combinations.

4. נָ | נִ | נוֹ | מוֹ | נַ | שָׁ

5. תָּ | מְ | תוֹ | בַּ | נִ | לְ

6. נִ | תָּ | מָ | תוֹ | אוֹ | תוֹ

7. לְ | בְּ | נָ | נִ | דָם | דֶן

Miss Elegant is the name of this women's store.
Circle all the נ letters you find.

Meet the הֵא (Hay)

Your teacher will help you meet these ה words.

הַלְלוּיָה

הָמָן

הַבְדָּלָה

הַגָּדָה

Practice these ה letters.

ה ה   ה ה   ה ה   ה ה   ה ה   ה ה .1

Cross out the letters that don't match the first letter on each line.

ﬨ ה   ה ה   ﬨ ה   ה ה   ה ה   ה ה .2

שׁ שׁ   א שׁ   שׁ שׁ   ב שׁ   מ שׁ   שׁ שׁ .3

א א   מ א   שׁ א   א א   א א   א א .4

מ מ   ם מ   שׁ מ   מ מ   מ מ   מ מ .5

When the ה is at the beginning or middle of a word it says "h".
When the ה is at the end of the word, it is often silent.

Vowel Review

Practice the letter  with all the vowels we've learned so far.

הָ הֹ הוּ הִ הֶ הָ הַ

Now sound out the Hebrew on each line. Circle all the sounds that rhyme with the one in the colored box.

מָ	לוּ	מְ	נַ	דוּ	דָ	.1
דָ	תְ	דְ	הוּ	בֶ	לִ	.2
בָ	דְ	מָ	נִ	אַ	הִ	.3
שׁוֹ	לִ	תוֹ	הָ	בְ	מוֹ	.4
הוֹ	נָ	הִ	מָ	הוֹ	אֶ	.5

Here is a movie poster in a video store window. Can you find any ה letters? Do you know the name of this movie?

Meet the רֵישׁ (Reish)

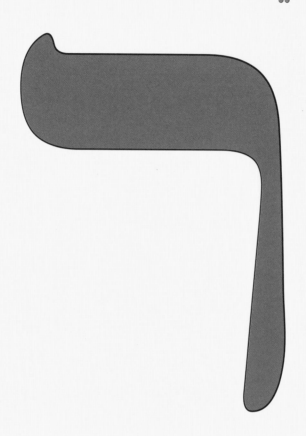

Your teacher will help you meet these ר words.

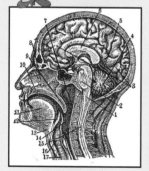

רֹאשׁ   רַעֲשָׁן   רִמּוֹנִים   רַב

Trace these ר letters and then make two of your own.

Practice these ר letters by saying each aloud.

ר ר ר ר ר ר ר .1

Draw a box around the ר letters, a circle around the ד letters and a triangle around the ה letters.

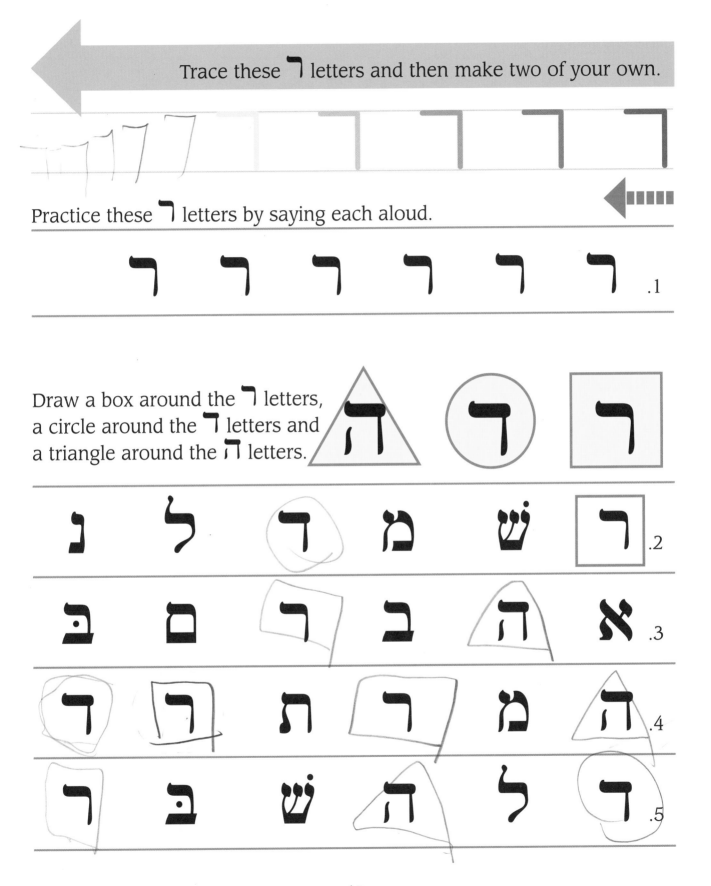

נ ל ד מ שׁ ר .2

ב ם ר ב ה א .3

ד ר ת ר מ ה .4

ר ב שׁ ה ל ד .5

40

The symbol under the ר is a vowel. It makes the sound "eh."

The name of this vowel is *segol*.

Practice the letters you know with the new vowel ◼ and with all the vowels you know.

מֶ	שֶׁ	דֶ	לֶ	בֶ	רֶ	.1

Can you sound out this word?

מֶ	אִ	בּוֹ	תֶ	.2
אֶ	אָו	אַ	אֶ	.3
רוֹ	רֶ	רִ	רָ	.4

מוֹרֶה

41

This words on this can of kosher scouring powder (cleanser) is written in Hebrew letters, but it is actually in Yiddish. Yiddish is a language of the Jews of Eastern Europe that is made up of lots of different languuages, including Hebrew, German, French and Italian.

Circle all the ר letters on this can.

Meet the וָו (Vav)

Your teacher will help you meet these וֹ words.

וְכֹחַ   וָו   וַשְׁתִּי   וֶרֶד

Trace these **ו** letters and then make two of your own.

ר   ו   ו   ו   ו

Practice these **ו** letters.

ו   ו   ו   ו   ו   .1

Practice these letters by saying their sounds.

ה   ר   ן   ל   ד   ו   .2

ו   ד   א   נ   ו   מ   .3

נ   ר   ת   ו   שׁ   ל   .4

ת   א   ו   בְּ   בּ   תָּ   .5

ה   ו   שׁ   ם   ל   שׁ   .6

44

Practice the letters you know with all the vowels you know.

1. וֵ דָ נְ לוֹ לְ נָ תֶ מַ

2. בָ וְ אָ נֶ הוֹ בְ

3. אֶ לְ דוֹ רוֹ שֵ נָ

4. בָ נוֹ תֶ לָ שׁוֹ תִ

5. נֶ לְ ר מוֹ נְ שָׁ

Can you sound out these words?

וֶרֶד

רַב

Here is a word you may not know. Can you guess what it means?

שֶׁמֶשׁ

45

𐤇𐤀𐤓𐤅𐤀𐤓𐤃

הרוורד

هارفارد

HARVARD

This is a T-shirt from Harvard University. Can you guess what other languages appear on this shirt beside Hebrew and English? Circle the letters.

Meet the טֵית (Tet)

Your teacher will help you meet these ט words.

טֶבַע   טוֹב   ט"וּ בִּשְׁבָט   טַלִית

Trace these letters and then make two of your own.

Practice these letters.

Match these letters.   Connect these sound-alike letters.

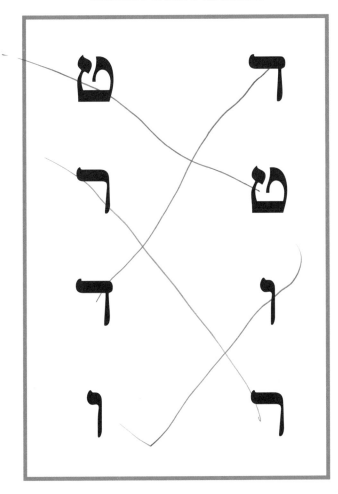   

Your teacher will help you with this new vowel. Sometimes it makes the sound "eh," and sometimes the sound "ei."

The name of this vowel is *tzereh*.

Practice the letters you know with the new vowel ⬛ and with all the vowels you know.

					.1
לֵ	שֵׁ	טֶ	רֵ	מֵ	טֶ

				.2
לוֹ	טֶ	בְּ	מָ

				.3
טֶ	טוֹ	טָ	טִ

				.4
לֵ	מְ	רֵ	דוֹ

Can you sound out this word?

נֵר

49

Here's a local hardware store. Circle all the ט letters you find. Don't forget to check the small type.

Meet the עַיִן (Ayin)

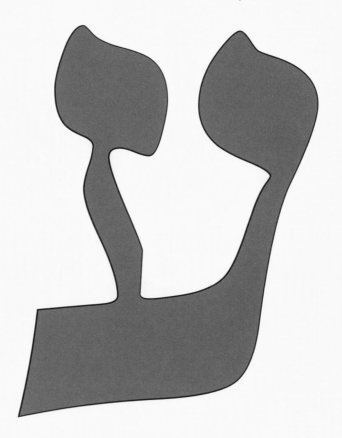

Your teacher will help you meet these ע words.

עַם

עֵץ חַיִּים

עוֹלָם

עֵץ

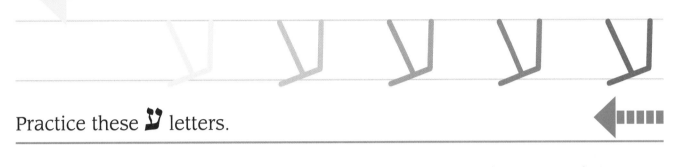

Trace these ע letters and then make two of your own.

Practice these ע letters.

ע ע ע ע ע ע .1

Draw a box around the ע letters, a circle around the ט letters and a triangle around the א letters.

ב △א ד ע ל ט .2

נ שׁ א ר ע ב .3

א ע ת ט מ ע .4

ע ל שׁ א ד מ .5

52

1. עַ עִ עֹ עֻ עָ עֵ

2. שֶׁ טֶ דּ נוֹ וְ רְ

3. בּוֹ תֶ לְ בְּ

4. הַ בָ עָ נַ

5. נָ טַ שֶׁ לוֹם עָ

Can you sound out this word?

עוֹלָם

Sound out the Hebrew on each line.
Color the circle if all the vowels on the line sound the same.

6. ◯ מֶ עָ רְ לְ הֵ

7. ◯ עָ בָ טַ רָ אַ

8. ◯ וְ נְ טֶ דּ אֶ

Just as in your city, there is a lot of building going on in Jerusalem. This new area is in the city center. Circle all the ע letters in this sign.

Meet the כָף (Kaf)

Your teacher will help you meet these כ words.

כָּבוֹד

כֹּתֶל

כִּפָּה

כַּרְפַּס

Practice these כ letters.

כ   כ   כ   כ   כ   כ   .1

Practice these letters by saying its sound.

ל   כ   ט   ד   ב   כ   .2

ת   ר   א   ע   נ   מ   .3

כ   נ   שׁ   ת   ב   ו   .4

ט   ו   ה   ד   ב   א   .5

ר   ע   ן   ם   ל   כ   .6

56

This is a כ *sofit*. *Sofit* means "end." This ך is only used at the end of a word. Sometimes it looks like ךָ and sometimes like ךְ.

This is a כ, another version of the כ. It makes the sound you make when you clear your throat.

Practice sounding out these combinations.

1. כָ הְ בֶ לוֹ אֶ רוֹ

2. בֶּ וְ כוּ שַׁ מַ

3. אַךְ כַּךְ מִן

4. לֶךְ תּוֹךְ בֵּן

Can you sound out this word?

עַם

57

Welcome to the Star Laundry in Jerusalem.
Find and circle all the **כ** letters in the laundry's sign and window.
Don't forget the **ך** *sofit*.

Meet the יוּד (Yud)

Your teacher will help you meet these י words.

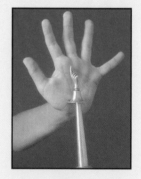

יוֹסֵף   יְרוּשָׁלַיִם   יִשְׂרָאֵל   יָד

Trace these **׳** letters and then make two of your own.

ד　　ד　　ד　　ד　　ד

Practice these **׳** letters.

י　　י　　י　　י　　י　　י

.1

Match these letters. | Connect these sound-alike letters.

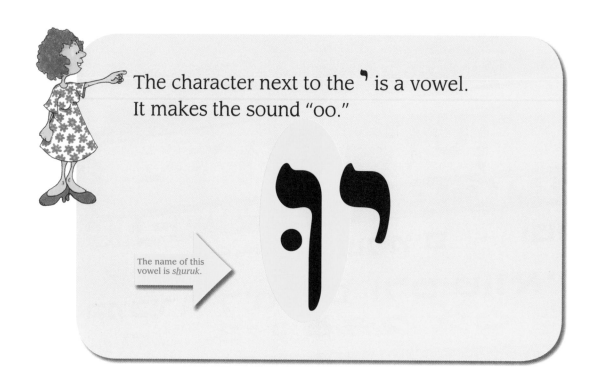

The character next to the **׳** is a vowel.
It makes the sound "oo."

The name of this vowel is *shuruk*.

וּ

Practice the letters you know with the new vowel **וּ** and
with all the other vowels you know.

נוּ	שׁוּ	בּוּ	מוּ	הוּ	יוּ	.1
יוֹ	כָ	כָּ	יְ	כְּ	טוּ	.2
דוֹ	טָ	לְ	מְ	רֶ	דוּ	.3
תוּ	אוּ	יֶ	עֶ	כָ	הֶ	.4

Let's visit this spice shop. What are your favorite spices? Circle the **י** letters on this sign.

Meet the חֵית (<u>H</u>et)

 Your teacher will help you meet these ח words.

| חֲבֵרִים | חֹשֶׁן | חַלָה | חֲנֻכִּיָה |

Trace these ח letters and then make two of your own.

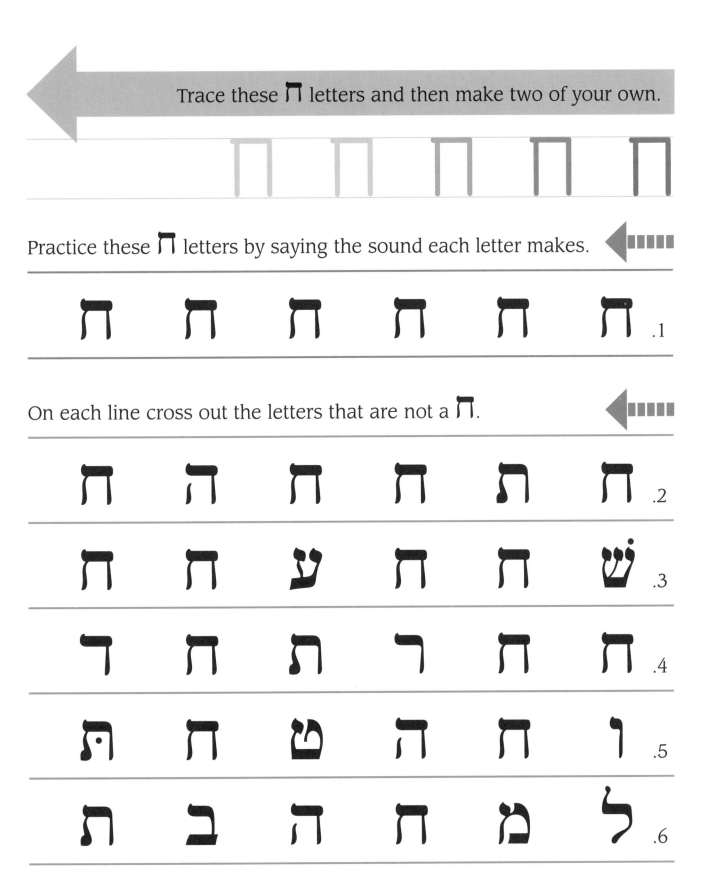

Practice these ח letters by saying the sound each letter makes.

ח   ח   ח   ח   ח   ח .1

On each line cross out the letters that are not a ח.

ח   ה   ח   ח   ת   ח .2

ח   ח   ע   ח   ח   שׁ .3

ד   ח   ת   ר   ח   ח .4

ת   ח   ט   ה   ח   ו .5

ת   ב   ה   ח   מ   ל .6

64

Practice these sounds.

.1   חוֹ   הֹ   הֹ   תָּ   לְ   מֶ   ר

.2   בּוּ   כּוּ   דֶ   נַ   אוּ   עוֹ

.3   חֶ   כֶ   חוּ   הֹ   כּוּ   חָ

.4   דוֹר   חָב   כֶּן   לוֹא

.5   אֶשׁ   עֵד   בַּת   בַּר

Can you sound out these words?

חַלָה

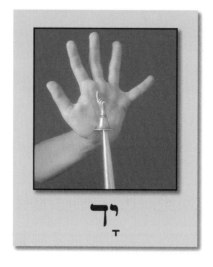

יָד

אֶחָד

65

Buy your lottery ticket here. The banners say that 18 people became millionaires in one month.

Circle the ה letters on these banners.

Meet the סָמֶךְ (Samekh)

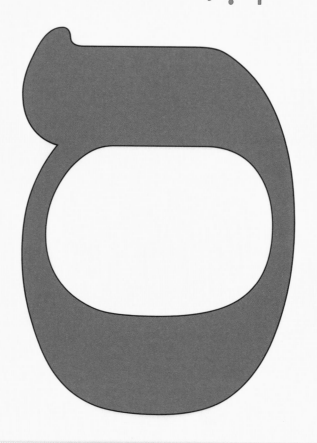

Your teacher will help you meet these ס words.

סִדּוּר	סִינַי	סְבִיבוֹן	סֻכָּה

Practice these ס letters.

ס   ס   ס   ס   ס   ס   .1

Draw a box around the ח letters,
a circle around the ס letters and
a triangle around the ו letters.

ח   א   ס   ו   ל   ⊙ס .2

נ   ו   א   ר   ע   ח .3

א   ס   ו   חו   מ   ו .4

ו   ל   ח   ס   ח   מ .5

The symbol next to the letter **ס** is a vowel. It says "oh."

The name of this vowel is _holom haser_.

Practice, practice and more practice.

מְ	רֶ	דֹ תָ	לָ	סֹ	.1
סוּ	כוֹ נְ	אֱ	רֹ	יוֹ	.2
לָ	חֹ תֶ	הֹ תֱ	אֹ	מְ	.3
נָ	נָ	רֹ נֱ	בְ	הָ	.4
דָ	הוֹ	יֶ מוּ	מֶ	רוֹ	.5

This building is a central warehouse for textiles (fabric). Circle the ס letters on this sign.

Meet the שִׁין (Sin)

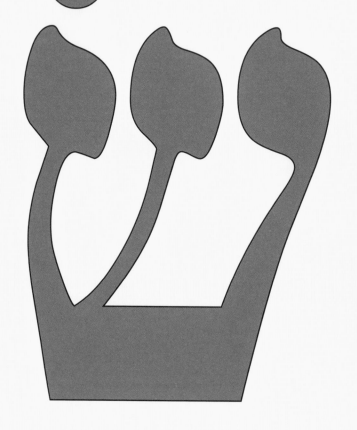

Your teacher will help you meet these שׁ words.

שָׂדֶה

שִׂיחָה

שִׂמְחַת תּוֹרָה

שִׂמְחָה

Trace these שׁ letters and then make two of your own.

Practice these שׁ letters.

שׁ שׁ שׁ שׁ שׁ שׁ .1

Match these letters.

Connect these sound-alike letters.

Practice these sounds.

שָׁ	שֶּׁ שֵּׁ	שָׁ שׁ	שׁ שִׁ	שׁ שׁ	שׁוּ	.1
חָ	שֶׁ שִׁ	שָׁ שׁ	עֵ	תּוֹ	סוּ	.2
בָ	אַ	כָ	כּוֹ	הָ	חוֹ	.3
בָ	וָ	כּ	טֶ	חָ	שִׁ	.4
חָ	כַּ	נִ	מָ	לֶ	ווֹ	.5

Can you sound out these words?

חֹשֶׁן

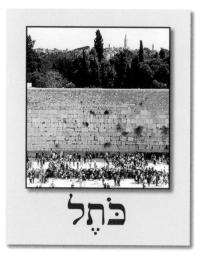

כֹּתֶל

טוֹב

ניידת טיפול נמרץ

INTENSIVE CARE UNIT

In America the group that helps people in emergencies and handles blood donations is called the Red Cross. In Israel the same group is called the Red Star. In Hebrew the Red Star is called Magen David Adom.

This is an ambulance that is being sent to Israel. Many American Jews collected the money to buy it for the Magen David Adom.

Find the one on this ambulance and circle it.

Meet the פֵּה (Peh)

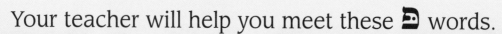

Your teacher will help you meet these פ words.

פֵּרוֹת (פְּרִי)   פָּרוֹכֶת   פּוּרִים   פֶּסַח

Trace these **פ** letters and then make two of your own.

Practice these **פ** letters by saying the sound each letter makes.

 פַ   פַ   פַ   פַ   פַ   פַ   .1

On each line circle the **פ** letters.

כ   מ   פַ   ר   שׁ   ה   .2

פַ   נ   ס   ע   פַ   ד   .3

ח   פַ   כּ   בּ   ע   א   .4

פַ   י   נ   פַ   ט   תּ   .5

בּ   כ   פַ   ה   ת   פַ   .6

76

This is a **פ** *sofit. Sofit* means "end." This **ף** is only used at the end of a word.

This is a **פ**, another version of the **בּ**. It makes the sound "F."

Practice sounding out these combinations.

.1 פֶּ פָ כָ בְ כ פֵ פֶ פַּ

.2 כַ כָ פֻ פֻּ כ פֻ פ

.3 פֹ פֶ פוּ פֶ פֻ

.4 אַף עוֹף תֹּף

Can you sound out this word?

שׁוֹפָר

77

Time for a snack. Falafel, steak and hamburgers are some of the choices at this snack shop. Circle all the ב letters you find. Make sure you check all the signs.

Meet the זַיִן (Zayin)

Your teacher will help you meet these ז words.

זֶרַע   זְמִירוֹת   זָהָב   זִכָּרוֹן

Trace these ז letters and then make two of your own.

Practice these ז letters.

      .1

Draw a box around the ז letters, a circle around the ו letters and a triangle around the נ letters.

      .2

      .3

      .4

      .5

80

The symbol under the letter וֹ is a vowel. It says "oo."

The name of this vowel is *kubbutz*.

Practice, practice and more practice.

טֻ	סֻ	כֻ	חֻ	נֻ	זֻ	.1
זֻ	זוּ	זוֹ	זִ	זֻ	זָ	.2

.3 לֻ עֻ מִ סַ עֻ לֻ

| | Can you sound out this word? | פֻּה וָ נֶר רַ | .4 |

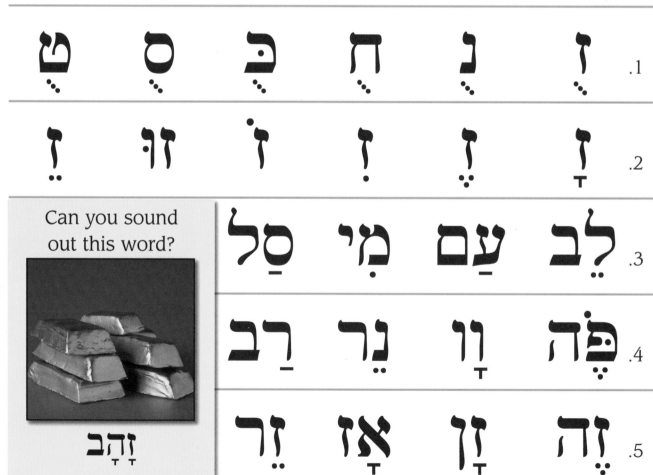

זָהָב

.5 זֶה זָן אֻ זֶר

81

המוזיאון לאמנות יהודית
ע"ש סר אייזיק
ולליידי אדית וולפסון

The Sir Isaac and
Lady Edith Wolfson
Museum of Jewish Art

Here we are at the Museum of Jewish
Art. Find and circle all the ו letters.

Meet the גִּימֶל (Gimel)

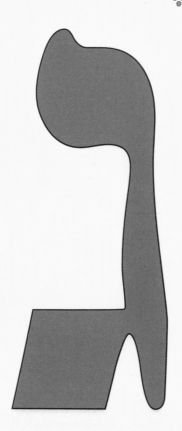

Your teacher will help you meet these גּ words.

גְּמִילוּת חֲסָדִים   גָּמָל   גֶּשֶׁם   גָּדוֹל

ג ג ג ג ג

Practice these ג letters.

ג ג ג ג ג ג .1

Match these letters.

Connect these sound-alike letters.

Sound out the Hebrew on each line. Circle all the sounds
that rhyme with the one in the colored box.

גִ	גֵ	גָ	גֶ	גוּ	גֵ	.1
עָ	לֶ	כְ	רְ	טֶ	שֵׁ	.2
יִ	זֶ	גֶ	מֶ	פִ	חִ	.3
פֶ	עָ	הֶ	גוֹ	תִ	סֹ	.4
פֶ	שַׁ	שָׁ	זִ	לֵ	דַ	.5

Can you sound out these גּ words?

גָּמָל

גֶּשֶׁם

גָּדוֹל

85

How about a field trip?
Circle all the **ג** letters in this sign.

Meet the
קוֹף (Kuf)

Your teacher will help you meet these ק words.

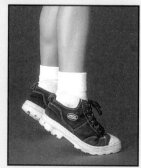

| קָטָן | קְהִלָּה | קָדוֹשׁ | קָדוֹשׁ |

Trace these ק letters and then make two of your own.

ק ק ק ק ק

Practice these ק letters by saying the sound each letter makes. ◀▪▪▪▪▪

ק ק ק ק ק ק .1

Sound out the letters on these lines and circle all the ק letters. ◀▪▪▪▪▪

ק ה שׁ ק ר כּ .2

ג ק שׁ פּ ק ד .3

ה ל ק ע ס ק .4

ק ט ח ז ו א .5

ג ק נ ק י ק .6

88

Sound out the Hebrew on each line. Color in the circle
if all the sounds on the line are the same.

	קוּ	קֵ	קָ	קֵ	◯ .1
	זֵ	זֵ	זַ	זָ	◯ .2
	גֹ	גֹ	גוֹ	גֹ	◯ .3
	פֵּ	כֵּ	פֵּ	פֵּ	◯ .4
	דֵ	דֵ	ר	דֵ	◯ .5

Your teacher will say a sound for each of these lines.
Be the first to circle it!

.6	בָ	ר	כֵ	מֵ	קֵ	סֵ
.7	עוֹ	פֵּ	יֵ	גֵ	וּו	דֵ
.8	קָ	זֵ	נֵ	וֵ	הֵ	כָ

89

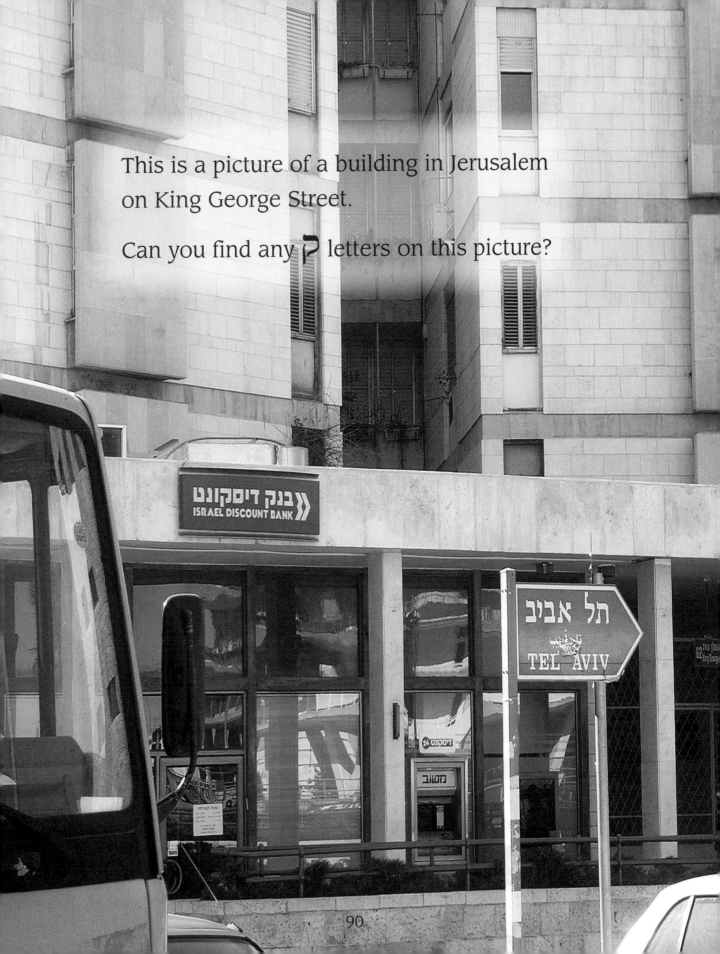

This is a picture of a building in Jerusalem on King George Street.

Can you find any ק letters on this picture?

Meet the צָדִי (Tzadi)

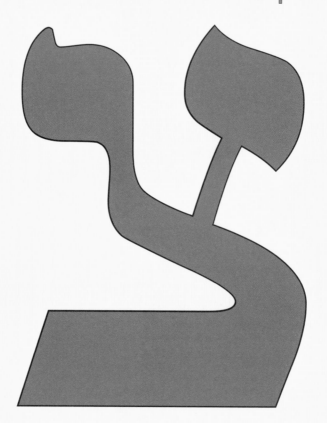

Your teacher will help you meet these צ words.

צֹאן   צְפַרְדֵעַ   צִיצִית   צְדָקָה

Practice these צ letters by saying the sound each letter makes.

      .1

Draw a box around the צ letters, a circle around the ע letters and a triangle around the א letters.

      .2

      .3

      .4

    .5

Circle the **צ** and draw a box around the **ץ**.

This is a **צ** *sofit*.
Sofit means "end."
This **ץ** is only used
at the end of a word.

צ	ע	ץ	צ	.1
ף	ץ	דּ	ו	.2
ץ	צ	א	צ	.3

Practice sounding out these combinations.

מִ	וַ	צִּ	סֶ	פְּ	צֶ	.4
לְ	אֵ	בָּ	חָ	מוֹ	כֶּ	.5
	נַ	דִּ	אַ	ם	.6
	לֶ	פֶּ	רָ	נוֹ	.7

Can you sound out this **צ** word?

צִיצִית

Bonus Points!!!
Try sounding out
these two "words."

בֵּץ עֵץ .8

93

This page is almost 300 years old. It comes from a Passover Haggadah that was written in Amsterdam in the year 1716.

The page teaches the fifteen steps of the Passover seder.

Look for all the צ letters. How many can you find?

The Alef-Bet

NAME	SOUND	SCRIPT	PRINT	LETTER
Nun	n			נ
Nun	n			ן
Samekh	s			ס
Ayin	silent			ע
Peh	p			פּ
Peh	f			פ
Peh	f			ף
Tzadi	tz			צ
Tzadi	tz			ץ
Kuf	k			ק
Resh	r			ר
Shin	sh			שׁ
Sin	s			שׂ
Tav	t			תּ
Tav	t			ת

NAME	SOUND	SCRIPT	PRINT	LETTER
Alef	silent			א
Bet	b			בּ
Bet	v			ב
Gimel	g			ג
Dalet	d			ד
Hey	h			ה
Vav	v			ו
Zayin	z			ז
Het	h			ח
Tet	t			ט
Yud	y			י
Kuf	k			כּ
Kuf	kh			כ
Kuf	kh			ך
Lamed	L			ל
Mem	m			מ
Mem	m			ם